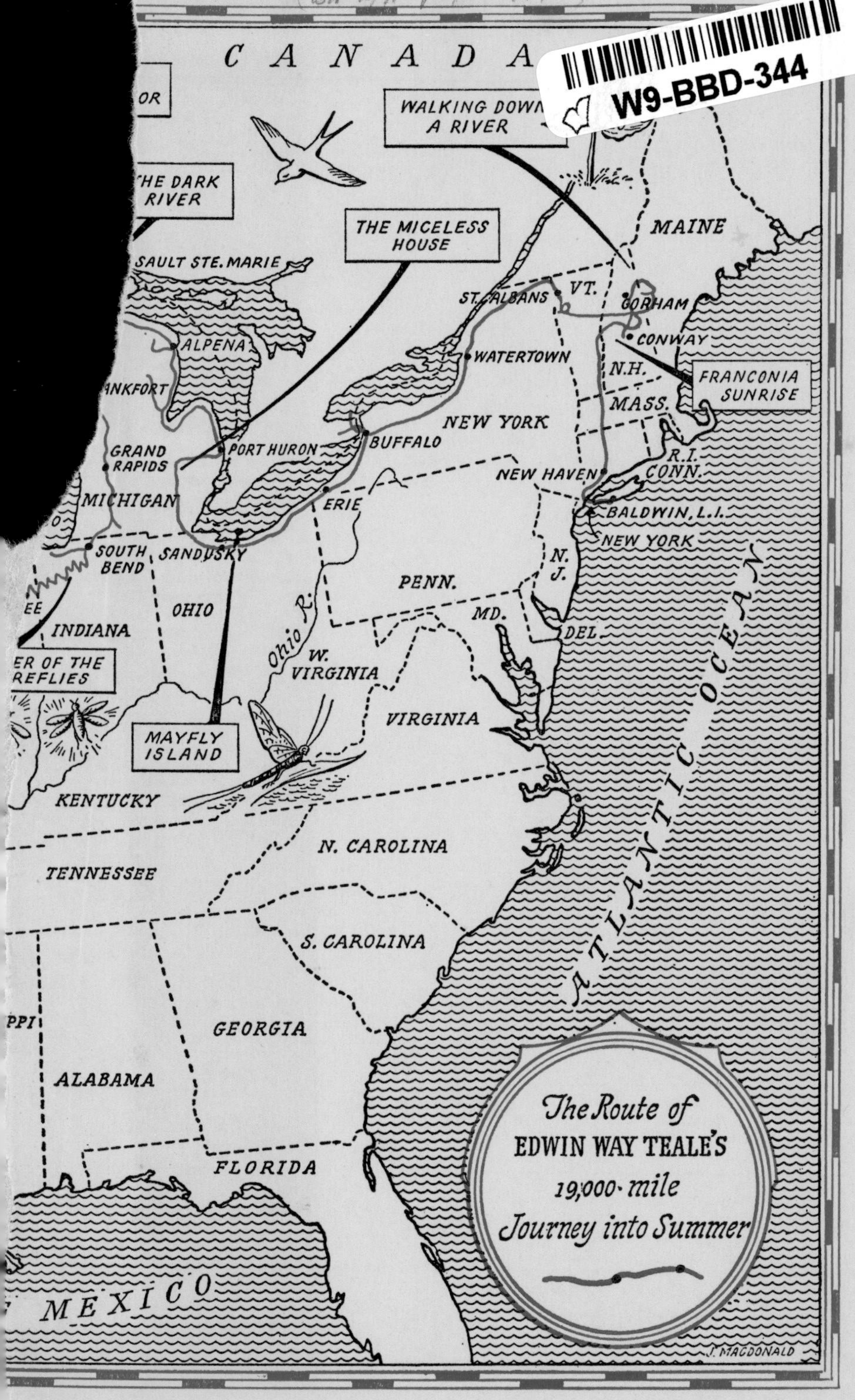
CANADA
WALKING DOWN A RIVER
THE DARK RIVER
THE MICELESS HOUSE
SAULT STE. MARIE
ALPENA
GRAND RAPIDS
MICHIGAN
PORT HURON
SOUTH BEND
SANDUSKY
INDIANA
OHIO
MAYFLY ISLAND
KENTUCKY
TENNESSEE
ST. ALBANS
VT.
MAINE
GORHAM
CONWAY
N.H.
FRANCONIA SUNRISE
MASS.
WATERTOWN
NEW YORK
BUFFALO
ERIE
R.I.
CONN.
NEW HAVEN
BALDWIN, L.I.
NEW YORK
N.J.
PENN.
MD.
DEL.
Ohio R.
W. VIRGINIA
VIRGINIA
N. CAROLINA
S. CAROLINA
GEORGIA
ALABAMA
FLORIDA
MEXICO
ATLANTIC OCEAN
The Route of
EDWIN WAY TEALE'S
19,000-mile
Journey into Summer
J. MACDONALD